C000142369

STAR MATHS PUZZLES & PROBLEMS

A fresh approach to using and applying maths

TERMS AND CONDITIONS

IMPORTANT – PERMITTED USE AND WARNINGS - READ CAREFULLY BEFORE USING

Minimum specification:
- PC or Mac with a CD-ROM drive and at least 128 Mb RAM
- Recommended screen resolution: 1280 × 1024 pixels. (See CD help notes for details.)
- Facilities for printing

PC:
- Windows 98SE or above
- Recommended minimum processor speed: 600 MHz

Mac:
- Mac OSX1. or above
- Recommended minimum processor speed: 500 MHz

For all technical support queries, please phone Scholastic Customer Services on 0845 6039091.

Anthony David and Julie Cogill

Authors
Anthony David and Julie Cogill

Development Editor
Niamh O'Carroll

Editor
Nicola Morgan

Assistant Editor
Margaret Eaton

Illustrations
Pages 12-31 & 45 © Wizzmedia

Pages 34-40, 42 & 43 © Rupert van Wyk / Beehive Illustration

Pages 6-10 © Blake Publishing / Pascal Press, originally published in *Targeting Maths Problem Solving Level 2* (Pascal Press, 2007)

Series Designer
Joy Monkhouse

Designer
Melissa Leeke

Text © 2008 Anthony David and Julie Cogill
© 2008 Scholastic Ltd

CD-ROM design and development in association with Wizzmedia

Designed using Adobe CS

Published by Scholastic Ltd
Villiers House, Clarendon Avenue,
Leamington Spa, Warwickshire CV32 5PR
www.scholastic.co.uk

Printed by Tien Wah, Singapore
1 2 3 4 5 6 7 8 9   8 9 0 1 2 3 4 5 6 7

ISBN 978-1407-10034-0

ACKNOWLEDGEMENTS
Extracts from the Primary National Strategy's *Primary Framework for Mathematics* (2006) www.standards.dfes.gov.uk/primaryframework © Crown copyright. Reproduced under the terms of the Click Use Licence.

The approved SMART Software Accreditation logo is a trademark of SMART Technologies.

Every effort has been made to trace copyright holders for the works reproduced in this book, and the publishers apologise for any inadvertent omissions.

British Library Cataloguing-in-Publication Data
A catalogue record for this book is available from the British Library.

Introduction

Children need to learn how to solve problems by using and applying mathematics in a variety of contexts. However, when the *Framework for teaching mathematics from Reception to Year 6* was published in 1999, the focus was very much on number and calculations. The 1999 Framework has objectives under the broad heading of 'Solving problems', sub-divided into three sections:

- Making decisions
- Reasoning and generalising about numbers and shapes
- Problems involving 'real life', money or measures

At this point the National Curriculum gave much more attention to 'Using and applying mathematics', building it into all of the mathematics attainment targets. One of the principal aims of the renewed Primary Framework in 2006 therefore was to give greater attention to using and applying mathematics through the five themes of:

- Solving problems
- Representing
- Enquiring
- Reasoning
- Communicating

Star Maths Puzzles and Problems is designed to provide opportunities for children to use and apply mathematics in line with these themes and objectives. Each title reflects progression within the five themes by providing problems that encompass the full range of problem-solving processes and skills. The ten interactive problems on the CD-ROM will involve children in reasoning and predicting outcomes, in communicating their results, and in solving problems and developing lines of enquiry. Additionally, they provide opportunities for children to use problem-solving strategies to help them investigate and understand the mathematical content of each problem. What's more, the activities are engaging and challenging for all ability levels and most can be used flexibly either with the whole class on an interactive whiteboard or in small groups working at a computer.

About the book

Each book includes a set of teachers' notes linked to the interactive activities on the CD-ROM. A range of additional support is also provided, including an introduction to problem-solving strategies such as 'look for patterns', an objectives grid, follow-up problems linked to the CD-ROM activities and a 'problems bank' designed to consolidate or assess children's grasp of each problem-solving strategy.

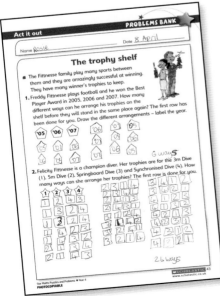

Strategies for using and applying

This book focuses on seven of the key strategies used in mathematical problem solving. Understanding these strategies will greatly assist children in making decisions about how to solve a problem, in organising and interpreting information and results and ultimately in finding solutions to problems. The strategies covered in this book include:

- Trial and improvement
- Read, plan, work, check
- Act it out
- Logical reasoning
- Make a list
- Draw a diagram
- Use a table

This section offers a rationale for each strategy, as well as issues to consider when children are starting to learn different strategies.

Teachers' notes

The teachers' notes cover the ten interactive activities on the CD-ROM. Each page of teachers' notes includes:

Learning objectives
Cover the strands and objectives of the renewed *Primary Framework for Mathematics* (2006) (using and applying objectives as well as objectives from other strands).

Problem-solving strategies
Suggestions for particular strategies to use to solve each CD-ROM problem.

Setting the scene
Setting the context of the problem and instructions for presenting the CD-ROM activity to the children.

Solving the problem
Notes on how to use a particular strategy to solve the CD-ROM problem.

Key questions
Probing questions to be used during the activity, sub-divided by the five themes of using and applying mathematics (see page 4 for further information).

Differentiation
Adapting the activity for more or less confident learners.

Follow up
Getting the children together to consolidate the learning, using practical activities and the related 'follow-up problems' activity sheets.

Problems bank
References to problems bank sheets (see below).

Annotations
At-a-glance instructions for using the CD-ROM activity.

Problems bank

For children to be able to find solutions in unfamiliar situations, they need to have experienced a wide variety of problems and puzzles and be able to call upon a bank of strategies with which to solve them. The 'problems bank' offers a range of problems designed to develop children's understanding of puzzles and problems and build up their use of strategies to solve them. The grid on pages 32–33 breaks down each problem by strategy or objective to help you to select appropriate problems.

About the CD-ROM

Each CD-ROM contains ten inspiring interactive activities designed to motivate and build children's confidence in solving maths problems and puzzles. Each activity is also designed to practise and reinforce one of the seven problem-solving strategies identified on pages 6–10. The problems are multi-faceted so that the children can return to them over and over again.

The CD-ROM also includes a Teacher zone containing editable objective grids, planning grids and printable versions of the follow-up problems and 'problems bank' activity sheets. Some additional 'problems bank' activities have also been supplied for further support and reinforcement.

Trial and improvement

Rationale

In using 'trial and improvement' as a problem-solving strategy, children must be able to hazard a good guess. This strategy builds their understanding and confidence. It gives them a starting point when they can't find any other way to start finding a solution.

Teaching the strategy

Use 'trial and improvement' when there is no starting point in the information given. Children need to be able to make good estimates to use this strategy. They also need to understand how to check against the original information given.

1. **Determine which information is to be used**
   Ask the children to carefully read and assimilate the information given in the problem. Rule out any unnecessary information.

2. **Highlight important data**
   Discuss which information is to be used when determining an estimate.

3. **Estimate**
   This is a very important skill. Children must have a feel for where their answers will lie. Large numbers or small? Will it be more or less than any information in the problem text? Ask the children what is reasonable.

4. **Check**
   Test the estimate against the information in the problem. If the need is to add the estimates, will the children reach the correct total? Checking is most important and must be seen to be part of the solution.

5. **Adjust up or down**
   When the first estimate proves to be incorrect, discuss how to determine whether estimates need to be larger or smaller. What information helps make these decisions? Guide children through the selection of second estimates, encouraging them to read the problem again.

6. **Working**
   Insist that all working out is left in place as a record of the children's thinking. In problem-solving exercises it is important to see how the process progressed. Give part marks for incorrect answers if working out is in place.

7. **Explain**
   Ask children to explain how they arrived at their estimates and how they solved the problem.

Links to

Dominoes
pages 12-13

Mother Bird
pages 24-25

Read, plan, work, check

Rationale

Learning how to structure an investigation is an integral part of developing mathematical thinking. The 'read, plan, work, check' strategy involves understanding and clarifying the question, selecting and using a strategy to solve the problem, working out a solution and checking the solution in terms of the original question. The use of this strategy can lay a firm foundation in the development of problem-solving skills.

Teaching the strategy

Refer to each of the following steps as you work through the problem with the children.

1. **Read the problem with understanding**
   Carefully read the problem and assimilate the information given. Encourage the children to underline important words. Ask: *What do you have to find out? What facts will help you to answer the question?*

2. **Make a plan**
   Encourage children to think carefully about what they need to do in order to solve the problem. Ask: *What are the different steps to this problem? What operations will you need to use?* Invite some children to tell the class how they plan to solve the problem.

3. **Work out the problem**
   Explain that all working out should be left in place as a record of the solution process. Children often think that their working out should be dispensed with if it is incorrect, but you should emphasise that in problem solving the *way* in which a solution is achieved is important.

4. **Check the answer**
   Encourage the children to re-read the problem and check it against their solutions. Pose a variety of other problems that allow children to practise this strategy.

Links to

Making tracks
pages 14–15

Logical reasoning

Rationale

In using 'logical reasoning' to solve problems, children consider many pieces of information and decide on a systematic method of utilising this information. This involves deciding which piece comes first, 'what is not' as well as 'what is' and how to reach the solution step by step.

Teaching the strategy

There are a number of strategies which come under the umbrella of solving problems by 'logical reasoning'. These include drawing a grid or a matrix, using a diagram, and considering all the information. Chiefly, the children must understand what they are being asked, what information is to be used and in what order it should be utilised.

1. **Read the problem with understanding**
   Highlight the actual question. This is the most important step, as the question and the data often contain tricks or twists that can confuse children.

2. **Decide on the data to be used**
   Decide what is known and what needs to be found out. Use a highlighter, leaving out unnecessary words.

3. **Decide on the strategy to be used**
   - Draw a grid or matrix and utilise a system to mark 'what is' and 'what is not'.
   - Use a diagram to position information so that it can be more easily understood.
   - Make a list. This strategy will simplify the data in the problem so that it can be seen more concisely. Consider all known information about the problem.

4. **Written work**
   Apply the strategy. The strategies all require some writing down of information. Insist that the children write down their working and can communicate this when asked to.

Links to

Magic boy: letters
pages 16–17

Mother Bird
pages 24–25

Star Quest
pages 26–27

Magic girl: tins
pages 28–29

Act it out

Rationale

'Act it out' is similar to 'draw a diagram' in some ways, but it involves the use of objects to clarify the solving of the problem. The use of objects makes it easy to move data around without committing pencil to paper and needing to erase or start again. Being active also makes children more likely to remember the process used, and then be able to use it again.

Teaching the strategy

When choosing suitable classroom objects to use when applying this strategy, consider the following:
- Squared paper - when designs, regular layouts, areas or perimeters are involved.
- Coloured pencils - when data needs to be shown differentially.
- Cubes - are usually part of the given data of the problem.
- Cards - when small pieces of paper need to be moved about separately.
- Measuring equipment - when experimentation with various sizes is necessary.
- Water, sand - often used in measuring mass and volume.
- String - when length is part of the data.

The main skills required to successfully utilise this strategy are as follows:

1. **Ability to read instructions carefully**
   Be sure to explain what is required in tasks that have complex instructions. The rules must be followed fully.

2. **Ability to demonstrate the solution**
   Children need to be able to demonstrate and/or explain their solution as they will have no evidence of the different moves they have made with concrete objects.

3. **Perseverance**
   For some children this is a real issue as many only want to finish quickly with a solution at the ready. The need to begin again, try another way, learn something and apply what is learned to another attempt is paramount here. Reward children who keep persevering to reach a solution.

Links to

Magic boy: letters
pages 16-17

Magic girl: tins
pages 28-29

Sven
pages 30-31

Make a list

Rationale

Setting out information in an orderly fashion guides children to think and work systematically. When a list is made, a pattern will often emerge and the solution may come more easily if this is pointed out. Making a list is therefore a step towards finding a pattern to solve similar problems in the future.

Teaching the strategy

Whenever a strategy is not obvious, making a list is a way to see what the information is saying. Also, when all possibilities need to be recorded and counted we make a list. Working systematically is necessary so that all possibilities can be seen to be covered. Focus on the following skills as you work through the problem.

1. **Work systematically**
   Children must be able to decide on a starting point, then work systematically through each item, exhausting all possibilities for that item before moving on to another piece of information. For example, to answer the question 'How many three-digit numbers can be made with the digits 345?' they should start with

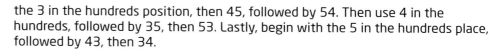

the 3 in the hundreds position, then 45, followed by 54. Then use 4 in the hundreds, followed by 35, then 53. Lastly, begin with the 5 in the hundreds place, followed by 43, then 34.

2. Physically set out the list
Children will realise that they need space for the list to expand down the page. In some situations, extra paper may need to be supplied. Teachers should introduce scaffolds if required.

3. Visualise/estimate
Children need to visualise possibilities, then they will have a good idea when they have covered them all.

4. Recognise repeat combinations
Ensure that the children understand that there will be repeats, which are not included unless the problem requires it. For example, A with B is the same as B with A, except where the order of the items makes a difference in the combination and should therefore be included.

5. Create a table
Lists may be made into tables, especially where more confident learners are ready to recognise this step. Unlike lists, a table has more than one column, with a heading for each column.

Links to

Monkey matters
pages 18-19

I-scream lady
pages 22-23

Draw a diagram

Rationale
Drawing a diagram helps children to demonstrate what they know about a problem. By drawing a picture of the data, they produce a concrete version of the information they need in order to solve the problem. The problem itself will become clearer, and a solution should become more readily apparent.

Teaching the strategy
Refer to each of the following steps as you work through the problem with the children.

1. Choose the diagram type
There are several different types of diagram to choose from. These include number lines, pizzas (for fractions), simple drawings of objects, and tree diagrams. The most suitable diagram to use will depend on the nature of the problem to be solved.

2. Convert data to a visual format
The children should use plenty of space on their sheets of paper (or individual whiteboards) and leave the diagram in place for marking and sharing. Give credit for all good attempts at drawing the diagram to encourage the children to place importance on 'process' as well as 'solution'.

3. Check the answer
Encourage the children to check their solutions by going back to the original data to be sure that it has all been correctly understood.

Links to

Monkey matters
pages 18-19

4. Explain the solution
The children's ability to verbalise the solution and answer questions about it will demonstrate their level of mathematical understanding. Ask questions such as: *Why did you choose the branching tree diagram? How did you use it to show the number of variations that are possible?*

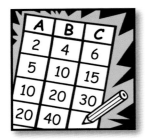

Use a table

Rationale

Making organised lists or tables involves working methodically. Most children start off recording their problem-solving efforts in a very haphazard way. The 'use a table' strategy leads children to organise their thinking, if they systematically progress through a problem. The strategy also helps them to organise information so that all of the possibilities of a solution are set out and easily viewed.

Teaching the strategy

There are several ways of using the 'use a table' strategy. These range from tables of numbers to help solve problems, to the type of tables with ticks and crosses that are often used in logic problems. Tables can also be an efficient way of finding number patterns. The following points should be noted when teaching problem solving using this strategy:

1. **Work methodically**
   Children must be able to decide on a starting point for their table and then work methodically to complete it. Ask questions such as: *What information do you want to know? How might a table help you find it?*

2. **Physically set out the table**
   Ask the children: *How many columns should your table have? What should the labels be?* Encourage them to draft different options for their tables at first (or, if necessary, provide them with some prepared templates as a starting point). Most children should quickly progress to the point where they no longer need prepared table templates, while others might require this support for longer.

3. **Visualise/check**
   The purpose of a table is to help the children visualise the problem. If the table requires the listing or breaking down of several options, encourage the children to organise their tables so that they can easily check that all possibilities have been exhausted. Clear working will also help to show where errors are occurring.

4. **Share the solution**
   Setting out the information in a table will help children to present the answer to a problem and to share their solution with others. It can also lead to further interrogation of data generated on the table.

Links to

Worm farm
pages 20–21

Activity no.	Activity title	Page no.	Learning objectives as taken from the Primary Framework for Mathematics		Problem-solving strategies
1	Dominoes	12	Using and applying	Solve one-step and two-step problems involving numbers	Trial and improvement
2	Making tracks	14	Using and applying	Choose and carry out appropriate calculations, using calculator methods where appropriate	Read, plan, work, check
			Measuring	Measure and calculate perimeters	
3	Magic boy: letters	16	Using and applying	Represent a puzzle or problem using statements; use these to solve the problem	Act it out Logical reasoning
4	Monkey matters	18	Using and applying	Represent a puzzle or problem using diagrams	Draw a diagram Make a list
			Handling data	Answer a question by identifying what data to collect	
5	Worm farm	20	Using and applying	Represent a puzzle or problem using number sentences, statements or diagrams; use these to solve the problem	Use a table
			Handling data	Analyse and interpret the data in tables	
6	I-scream lady	22	Using and applying	Suggest a line of enquiry and the strategy needed to follow it	Make a list
			Handling data	Answer a question by identifying what data to collect; organise, present, analyse and interpret the data in tables, diagrams, tally charts, pictograms and bar charts, using ICT where appropriate	
7	Mother Bird	24	Using and applying	Suggest a line of enquiry and the strategy needed to follow it	Logical reasoning Trial and improvement
8	Star Quest	26	Using and applying	Identify and use patterns, relationships and properties of numbers	Logical reasoning
9	Magic girl: tins	28	Using and applying	Report solutions to puzzles and problems, giving explanations and reasoning orally	Act it out Logical reasoning
10	Sven	30	Using and applying	Report solutions to puzzles and problems, giving explanations and reasoning orally	Act it out

Dominoes

Setting the scene

This is a group or paired activity. Eight dominoes have been used to make the pattern displayed at the top of the screen. The children must use the other eight dominoes to copy the pattern before the moon disappears. Click on a domino to select it, then either place it on the pattern or click on the 'rotate domino' button to turn it before placing it. The children should click on the 'I'm finished' button when the pattern is complete.

Solving the problem

Much of this problem will be solved by trial and improvement, with the children randomly placing dominoes in an attempt to match the patterns. Encourage them to look for patterns before placing the dominoes. There should always be some dominoes that can be placed quickly; as the children become more accustomed to pattern-making, the faster they will get. Encourage them to look for the dot patterns and to use one side of the domino as a starting point. For example, if a domino has 3 and 5 dots, players should look for dominoes with 5 dots in the shape. If it has a complementary '3 half', then it can be used to repeat the pattern in the new grid.

Key questions

Enquiring: *Are there any dominoes that can be placed vertically? Which dominoes do you think will be easiest to place? Why?*
Reasoning: *Are you sure that you have placed the domino in the right place? How are you sure?*
Communicating: *Which dominoes will you need to rotate? Can you prove that you are correct? Do the patterns match?*

Differentiation

Less confident: Support the children with actual sets of dominoes. Tell them to ignore the timer so that they can look for patterns without the pressure of having to complete the challenge in a set time.
More confident: Challenge the children to complete the pattern in as short a time as possible. Encourage teams to compete against each other to see who can be the fastest!

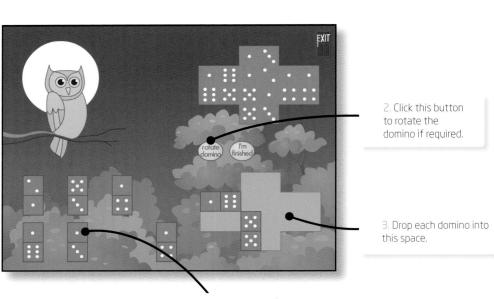

2. Click this button to rotate the domino if required.

3. Drop each domino into this space.

1. Click on a domino to drag or rotate it.

Name _____   Date _____

Dominoes

🔲 The owl has created two more puzzles. Cut out the dominoes at the foot of the page and organise them in the purple shape to match the patterns above.

1.

2.

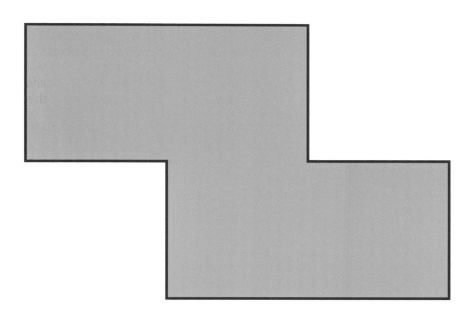

Making tracks

Setting the scene

This is a whole-class activity but it could alternatively be set up to work with pairs or groups.

To begin, the children must decide which is the longest track and how long it is. They should add all the lengths of each track to find it and then click on the correct track, within a time limit. If the correct track is selected, they must enter its length on the screen. Then they can 'drive' a lap round the track, using the arrow keys on the keyboard to direct the car. If they 'crash', the children can then try the activity again.

Solving the problem

The children should work out the perimeter of each track. This can be done by either adding up each side or by grouping lengths that are the same and multiplying. For example, if four sides of the track are 3km the children could reasonably multiply 3km × 4 = 12km. Emphasise that this is a more time-efficient method.

Key questions

Enquiring: *Are there any numbers that repeat? If so, what strategies could you use to quickly add these numbers? What strategies would you use to add other numbers quickly?*

Reasoning: *If some of the lengths of track are the same, can they be multiplied together?*

Communicating: *Do you all agree that the answer is correct? How are you able to prove your answer?*

Differentiation

Less confident: Emphasise that adding the tracks can be a case of multiple addition such as 4km + 3km + 4km + 3km. Encourage the children to look for patterns such as multiples of the same number and highlight that multiplying the same number is a faster method.

More confident: Challenge the children to find the length of the tracks in the shortest time possible. Ask them to explain what strategies they could use to speed up their calculations.

Which track is the longest?

2. Enter the length of the longest track. If correct, use the arrow keys to 'drive' a lap.

How many km is the track?

1. Click on the correct track.

Name _____ Date _____

Making tracks

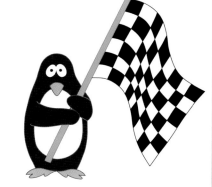

🔲 Look at the tracks. Fill in the missing lengths and work out the total distance for each track.

1.

15km

5km

_____km

_____km

10km

20km

Total distance _____

2.

6km   6km   4km

_____km

6km   6km   6km

6km   6km   8km

4km   4km

4km

_____km

20km

Total distance _____

🔲 Which is the longest track? _____

Magic boy: letters

- **Using and applying:** Represent a puzzle or problem using statements; use these to solve the problem

Act it out
Logical reasoning

Setting the scene

This activity is aimed at groups or paired workers. Magic boy will perform his amazing hat trick if the children are able to solve a puzzle at three levels. Each puzzle will involve a certain amount of 'acting out' or moving the on-screen letter bricks around until they are positioned in the correct sequence.

Solving the problem

This activity relies on both acting out the problem by moving the bricks around, and applying logical reasoning by breaking the problem into small chunks. It is a case of following each step and looking for discrete clues such as 'K is on the far right' (it is the furthest letter on the right). Highlight that each brick has a logical place within the sequence, and that the children should use the instructions not just to help place the bricks, but also to prove that they have the bricks in the correct place. This will enable them to answer the question and therefore choose the correct letter to type into the answer box.

Key questions

Representing: *How should you record where to place the bricks?*
Enquiring: *What key pieces of information are you being asked? Do you need to place all the bricks in order to answer the question? Is it possible to find a formula? Are you able to break the parts of the puzzle into smaller chunks?*
Communicating: *Do your bricks correspond to the instructions? Do they help you to answer the question?*

Differentiation

Less confident: There are three levels in this activity with A being the least difficult. Ensure the children start with level A before moving on to levels B and C. Provide the children with real letter bricks to help them to visualise the problem and to manually position the bricks into the correct sequence.
More confident: If there are two groups working against each other, use a timer to add an additional element of speed versus accuracy.

Use the alphabet block problems on page 17 to reinforce the problem-solving strategies used in this activity.

Page 36

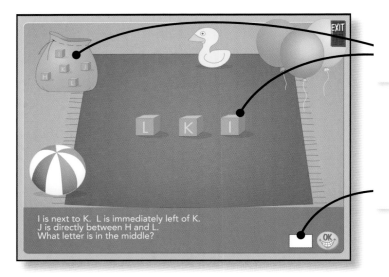

1. Drag each letter from the bag and drop it onto the red carpet.

2. Type the answer here.

I is next to K. L is immediately left of K. J is directly between H and L. What letter is in the middle?

Name _____   Date _____

Magic boy: letters

■ Cut out the letters at the bottom of the page and use them to solve these letter problems.

1. L is on the far right.

K is between I and H.

J is immediately right of H.

K is immediately right of I.

What letter is in the middle? _____

2. H is next to I.

J is immediately left of I.

K is directly between L and J.

What letter is in the middle? _____

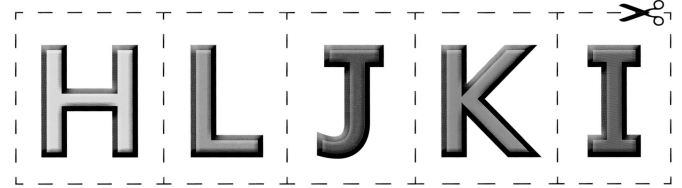

Monkey matters

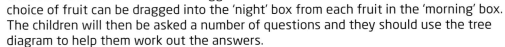

Setting the scene

This is a whole-class activity. The children must help the monkey
make choices by using a branching tree diagram. The monkey will
choose a number of different fruits for his menu for the day; this
number must then be typed into the box. To begin the tree
diagram, children must click on the purple 'start' dot and drag a
piece of fruit into the 'morning' box. This should be repeated
until all of the fruits have been dragged out. Then the second
choice of fruit can be dragged into the 'night' box from each fruit in the 'morning' box.
The children will then be asked a number of questions and they should use the tree
diagram to help them work out the answers.

  Once they have completed the monkey's menu they will be asked similar questions
about the clothes he is going to wear.

Solving the problem

Ask the children to work out the problem on paper or individual whiteboards first.
There can be a lot of combinations but the key is to look for patterns. They should
develop a strict pattern to follow when creating their tree diagram, as without
a systematic approach it will be difficult to prove that they have created all the
combinations. Work through the activity on the interactive whiteboard to check
answers.

Key questions

Representing: *How could you clearly show the data? What options are there to choose
from?*
Enquiring: *What information does the tree diagram begin to give you once you start to
create it?*
Communicating: *What is the answer to the problem? Are you happy with how it looks?
If not, how could you improve your diagram? What challenges arise when there are
many combinations?*

Differentiation

Less confident: Restrict the number of combinations to two and explain clearly that
fruit can be re-used (for example, morning – banana, night – banana). Use a whiteboard
and start with a branching diagram for two meals.
More confident: Add one more piece of fruit to the plate (for example, a pineapple).
Ask: *How many more combinations does this extra piece of fruit create?*

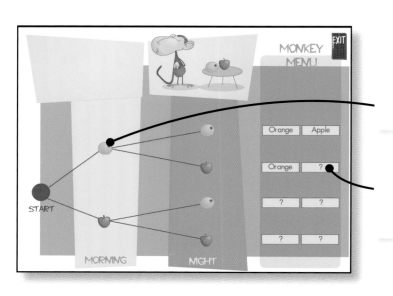

1. Drag out the fruit
to begin making a
branching tree diagram.

2. Add the missing
information –
encourage the children
to look for patterns.

Name _____   Date _____

Elephant enquiry

- Solve this 'Elephant enquiry' using a tree diagram.

- Edgar the Elephant washes, sleeps and eats in the morning and then again at night. How many variations can he have on his day? For example:

morning $\Big\langle$ wash
               sleep
               eat

answer _____

Start

Morning   **Night**

Worm farm

Setting the scene

This is a whole-class activity. The children's task is to help Billy, Milly and Willy collect as many worms as possible, in the time allowed. They will need to be quick to click on the worms as they poke their heads above the ground. When the worms have been collected, the children are asked to complete a table, and answer questions relating to it. To finish, they must help Tilly, the super worm collector, as she tries to beat the others in a real test of worm collecting!

Solving the problem

A table or chart is a way of displaying information. Help the children to spot patterns in the information they are given in the first few columns. Explain that, to complete the table, they need to either multiply the number of worms caught by the number of minutes or they can add the number of worms caught onto the previous answer. This will help them to predict the missing information that is needed to be able to answer the questions.

Key questions

Representing: *How would you record the data? Is this the best way to record it? What other method could you use?* (Perhaps a chart or graph.)
Reasoning: *Are you sure that you have filled in the table correctly? How can you prove that you are correct?*
Communicating: *Who is going to catch the worms? How did you work out how many worms were caught in the table?*

Differentiation

Less confident: Support the children by looking carefully at the pattern in the table. Explain that the table can be completed by adding on the same amount each time.
More confident: Challenge the children to extend the table beyond the grid. Ask: *How many worms could each child collect in an hour, or in ten hours?*

Follow up

The grids on page 21 are from other worm farms. The children should complete both grids, looking carefully at the number of minutes beneath each graph.

Problems bank

Page 38

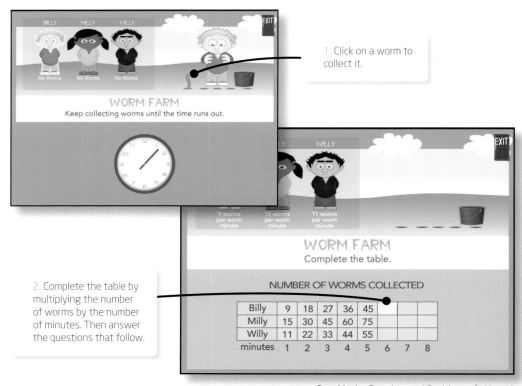

1. Click on a worm to collect it.

WORM FARM
Keep collecting worms until the time runs out.

WORM FARM
Complete the table.

2. Complete the table by multiplying the number of worms by the number of minutes. Then answer the questions that follow.

NUMBER OF WORMS COLLECTED

Billy	9	18	27	36	45			
Milly	15	30	45	60	75			
Willy	11	22	33	44	55			
minutes	1	2	3	4	5	6	7	8

Name _____ Date _____

Worm farm

- Look at these grids from other worm farms. Can you complete the grids? Each child collects the same number of worms every minute.

Imran collects 7 worms
Chloe collects 8 worms
Ali collects 11 worms
Zarah collects 6 worms

Imran				28					
Chloe		16							
minutes	1	2	3	4	5	6	7	8	9

Ali		33							
Zarah			30						
minutes	1	3	5	7	8	9	11	13	15

I-scream lady

Setting the scene

This is a whole-class activity. The I-scream lady has set up a shop and wants to offer the greatest range of flavours possible for her famous 'two-flavour ice creams'. Each cone holds two scoops of ice cream and she wants the children to work out the total number of combinations she can offer.

Solving the problem

Writing a list is an efficient method of work and should help the class to organise their thinking. Start by creating a number of random combinations and ask the children if they see any possible patterns. After a few combinations they should be able to see a pattern forming. Explain that although they could find each combination by randomly selecting flavours this would not support any predictions for the total number of combinations available and that there are only a finite number of varieties. Ask the children for any suggestions on what sort of line of enquiry they might take. Draw out any reasonable ideas before asking them to work out how many combinations there might be (there are 25 combinations in total). Ask the children to show how they were able to find the various combinations and what strategies they used. Identify the use of organised lists by demonstrating a pattern of answers such as:

banana strawberry
banana mint
banana vanilla, and so on.

Key questions

Representing: *What would be the best way to record the variety of ice-cream combinations?* (Using a list or table.)
Enquiring: *What methods will you use to find the answer? Are you able to predict the number of combinations?*
Communicating: *How many combinations are there? How can you prove that you are correct?*

Differentiation

Less confident: Use coloured cubes to represent the ice creams. Ask the children to make combinations from the cubes, encouraging them to follow a pattern. Tell them that there are 25 different combinations and challenge them to make as many as possible.
More confident: As an additional challenge, tell the children that for each combination, customers are asked if they would like a wafer as an optional topping. Ask: *How many combinations will this make?*

Learning objectives

● **Using and applying:** Suggest a line of enquiry and the strategy needed to follow it
● **Handling data:** Answer a question by identifying what data to collect; organise, present, analyse and interpret the data in tables, diagrams, tally charts, pictograms and bar charts, using ICT where appropriate

Problem-solving strategy

Make a list

Follow up

The children should use a similar strategy to solve the 'Mr Smoothy' problem on page 23. However, in this activity the number of combinations will be less because for each smoothie two fruits will be blended to create one drink (for example, banana/strawberry is the same as strawberry/banana).

Problems bank

Page 39

1. Drag the scoop and click on an ice-cream flavour to scoop it out then place it on the cone to select the flavour.

2. The list builds up as each combination is selected.

Name _____   Date _____

Mr Smoothy

Mr Smoothy wants to know how many different combinations he can make from the five-a-day fruits he has in his shop. Each smoothie is made from two different fruits. The fruits are: banana, strawberry, raspberry, mango and nectarine.

How many combinations does he have altogether?

_____

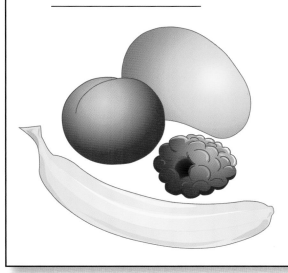

Fruit 1	Fruit 2

Remember, Mr Smoothy will be blending the fruits so it doesn't matter in what order they are placed – just how many different combinations there are, unlike with the I-scream lady.

Mother Bird

Setting the scene

Mother Bird has to collect worms for her chick and take them back to the nest. The aim of the activity is to collect the worms in the least number of steps. Display the first level and ask the children to work on squared paper to map out the position of the worms on a 10 × 10 grid. They should then work in groups to determine which path is the shortest for Mother Bird to take. Question the children to find out which group has found the shortest route, and invite one child from that group to demonstrate their solution on the interactive whiteboard, using the arrow keys on the keyboard to direct the bird.

From level 4, the worms begin to move around the screen, within tunnels. Use these levels with the whole class, discussing strategies for the shortest route before working through the activity together on-screen.

Solving the problem

Although this is a logical reasoning activity (finding ways to reach each worm via the shortest route so that the chick is reached most efficiently) it is, to begin with, solved with a degree of trial and improvement. Allow the children to try any strategies but encourage them to begin to look for patterns, emphasising that they are looking to find the shortest route.

Key questions

Representing: *How could you work out what is the best route?*
Reasoning: *How could you explain your route? What would be a bad route, and why?*
Communicating: *Who is best at describing a route in your group? How could you explain the game to somebody who is new? Are there any good hints you could give them to help? What would be the craziest route?*

Differentiation

Less confident: Encourage these children to create their own route. Once they have finished their first route, ask them how they could refine it to make it shorter or better.
More confident: The more attempts the children have at this problem, the faster they will be able to plot the shortest route. Even though they may have naturally seen an 'obvious route', ask them to describe in words the route they chose.

Follow up

Ask the children to use the grid on page 24 to find the shortest route to collect all the litter and take it to the recycling bin.

Problems bank

Page 40

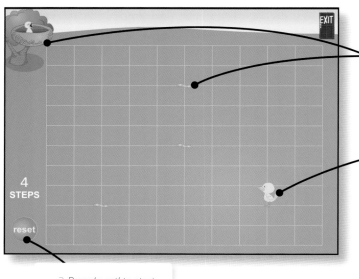

2. Collect all the worms and take them back to the nest by the shortest route.

1. Use the arrow keys to direct Mother Bird.

3. Press 'reset' to start again.

Name _____   Date _____

Litter collectors

■ Guide your team around the playground to collect all of the litter. Create a path that would be the shortest route to the bin. How many steps do you need to take?

Star Quest

Learning objective

● **Using and applying:** Identify and use patterns, relationships and properties of numbers

Problem-solving strategy

Logical reasoning

Setting the scene

This is a whole-class activity, based on a quiz show called Star Quest. Children must study the numbers on the grid before dragging the labels across, so that each column and each row has a correct label. When all the labels are in the correct place, one of the stars at the foot of the screen will light up. Once the children have collected all the stars, Bo-Bo the Clown will perform his famous 'jump through the hoop' trick.

Solving the problem

Ask the children to read the problem carefully and determine exactly what they will have to find – in this case, what numbers do they have and what properties are they aiming to match. Once they have done this, they should begin to work out what strategies can be used in order to accurately match the labels to the correct numbers. Encourage them to work carefully and to check their work, making sure each row and column is labelled correctly.

Key questions

Enquiring: *Look at the numbers. Are there any labels that are not appropriate?* (For example, 'these numbers are odd' would not apply if only even numbers are shown on the grid.)

Reasoning: *Are there any numbers that could use the same label? If so, which pair would you place it next to, and why?*

Communicating: *Is there more than one set of answers for each pair? How are you going to agree which answer to use? How can you prove your answer is correct?*

Differentiation

Less confident: Support the children in looking for clues, such as numbers that are factors or multiples or even/odd. Encourage them to read the labels carefully and make sure that both numbers match the label's statement. For example: 12 and 4 are both even numbers.

More confident: Point out that some of the numbers could have more than one label. Ask the children to note which numbers these are and what other labels they could have used. Then ask them to note which labels they cannot use at all.

Follow up

The children need to use the same strategy to work through the questions on page 27, using the labels correctly.

Problems bank

Page 41

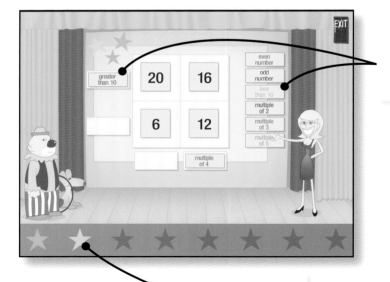

1. Drag the labels and drop them into the appropriate blank boxes.

2. Collect a star for every correctly labelled grid.

Name _____ Date _____

Star Quest

■ Look at these two sets of questions. Cut out the labels at the foot of the page and stick them into the correct places.

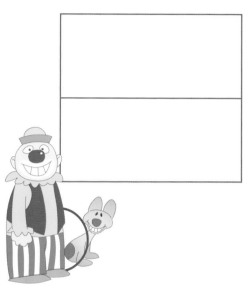

16	24
10	20

19	31
9	27

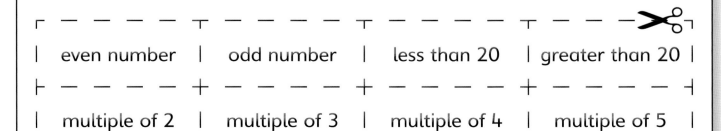

even number	odd number	less than 20	greater than 20
multiple of 2	multiple of 3	multiple of 4	multiple of 5

Magic girl: tins

Learning objective

● **Using and applying:**
Report solutions to puzzles and problems, giving explanations and reasoning orally

Problem-solving strategies

Act it out
Logical reasoning

Setting the scene

This activity is aimed at groups or paired workers. Magic girl will perform her amazing trick if the children are able to solve the puzzle from her magic bag, at three levels.

Tell the children that Simon has built a tower out of food tins and the children have to work out which tin to place where. They must follow the directions to accurately mark out where they should go and which tin is the correct answer. They have the option of changing the point of view and can move the tins around the screen until they feel confident that they are able to give a definite answer.

Solving the problem

This activity relies on both acting out the problem by moving the tins around, and applying logical reasoning by breaking the problem into small chunks. Once done, it is a case of following each step and looking for discrete clues such as 'the tin of beans is above the corn'.

The option of different perspectives can be useful when working with a group; it is important to highlight that there may be more than one way to approach the problem in order to get to the same answer. Emphasise the need for group members to listen to each other and collaborate to solve the problem.

Key questions

Representing: *How should you record where the tins go? Will changing the perspective help?*
Enquiring: *What key pieces of information are you being asked? Do you need to place all the tins in order to answer the question? Is it possible to find a formula?*
Communicating: *Are your marks or drawings accurate? Is another person able to follow them? Do they help you to answer the question?*

Differentiation

Less confident: Support the children by providing them with appropriate classroom resources (such as building bricks) which they can manually arrange into the correct positions.
More confident: If there are two groups working against each other, use a timer to add an additional element of speed versus accuracy.

Follow up

There are two similar problems to solve on page 29. Ask the children to work in pairs to help Simon find the answers.

Problems bank

Page 42

1. Select a point of view.

2. Drag the tins from the bag and rearrange as required.

3. Type your answer here.

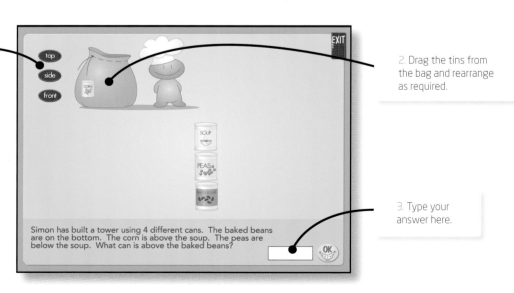

Simon has built a tower using 4 different cans. The baked beans are on the bottom. The corn is above the soup. The peas are below the soup. What can is above the baked beans?

Name _____   Date _____

Simon's tins

■ Work with a partner to solve the following problems.

■ Cut out the pictures of the tins to help you to work out the answers.

1. Simon has built a tower out of tins.
The tin of baked beans is on the bottom.
The soup is above the sweetcorn and the peas are below the sweetcorn.

What is above the baked beans? _____

2. Simon has built another tower out of tins.
The tin of baked beans is on the bottom and sweetcorn is above the peas. The soup is below the peas.

What is above the sweetcorn? _____

Sven

Learning objective

● **Using and applying:**
Report solutions to puzzles and problems, giving explanations and reasoning orally

Problem-solving strategy

Act it out

Setting the scene

This activity is for groups or pairs (although it could be used with the whole class).

Tell the class that Sven is playing against a robot who thinks he is impossible to beat. The children must help Sven to beat the robot by taking turns placing counters on the grid. Counters that are the same colour cannot be placed above, below or next to each other. The player who is able to place the last counter correctly is the winner.

Solving the problem

The game is simple to start with. However, the children should be encouraged to begin to look for patterns from the beginning. The robot will aim to 'box in' a player by strategically placing opposing colours near Sven's, therefore forcing him to use a repeated colour.

Key questions

Enquiring: *Are there any patterns that you should try to avoid? Do you have a strategy for 'trapping' your opponent?*
Reasoning: *Why have you placed the colour where you have? Are you just guessing?*
Communicating: *Did you win? If so, how? If you lost, how could you win next time? What do you need to do to improve your strategy?*

Differentiation

Less confident: Once learned, the game can be played on a basic 4 × 4 grid with three shapes such as circles, triangles and squares (eight of each). The children can then play in pairs against each other.
More confident: An additional level is to not allow colours above, below, to the side of, or diagonal to the same colour. This game is shorter but much more challenging.

Follow up

Ask the children to play Sven's new game on page 31 with a partner. It is based on the same concept as his original game, but instead of colours players use shapes to fill in the grid.

Problems bank

Page 43

It's Sven's turn.

1. Drag and drop a counter onto the game board.

2. Try to avoid being 'boxed in' by the robot, or use this strategy to beat him.

Name _____   Date _____

Sven

■ Sven has another similar game. He calls it 'Circles, triangles and squares'. The rules are the same except that in the 4 × 4 grid you place a shape rather than a colour. Play with a friend to see who can win!

Problems bank overview

Coin counting
Page 34

Problem-solving strategy: Trial and improvement

Being able to read the unusual names in puzzles and problems in not important. Make sure the children do not stop at reading names. Highlight the important information and check it at the end.

Linked to activity: Dominoes

Stickers
Page 35

Problem-solving strategy: Read, plan, work, check

Children are asked to work through a series of problems relating to number, including calculations involving fractions.

Linked to activity: Making tracks

Help the zoo
Page 36

Problem-solving strategy: Act it out

After they manipulate the straws to solve the placement of the fences, have the children draw in the fences for the solutions.

Linked to activity: Magic boy: letters

Properties of shapes
CD only

Problem-solving strategy: Logical reasoning

This worksheet gives practice at deciding 'what is' and 'what is not'. Knowledge of various shapes is tested.

Linked to activity: Magic boy: letters

In the garden
Page 37

Problem-solving strategies: Make a list

Each list is reading across the page. Monitor the children's responses - ask some children to read out their lists. Check for accuracy. Give less and less support as they attempt each problem on the page.

Linked to activity: Monkey matters

Handy trees 1
CD only

Problem-solving strategies: Draw a diagram

The children are given the structure of a tree diagram (set out vertically). They only need to put in labels and answer questions from their conclusions, which they should be encouraged to verbalise.

Linked to activity: Monkey matters

Handy trees 2
CD only

Problem-solving strategies: Draw a diagram

The children are given the structure of the tree diagram. They only need to put in labels and answer questions from their conclusions, which they should be encouraged to verbalise. The children should write the names of the different jobs on the branches and the names of the scout volunteers in the blank boxes provided. Unlike the tree diagram in 'Handy trees 1', this diagram is set out horizontally. Discuss the use of the two formats.

Linked to activity: Monkey matters

Dogs at work
Page 38

Problem-solving strategy: Use a table

Read the information carefully. After the children have worked their way through questions 1 to 3, ask them to complete the table in question 4.

Linked to activity: Worm farm

Problems bank overview

On the farm — Page 39

Problem-solving strategy: Make a list

Make sure that the children understand the setting out of the different lists. On the board, review how lists are filled in. Some work across and some work down. Discuss the appropriateness of this setting out. Check that the children are completing the lists correctly before they work on their own. The aim is to see that they learn the process of making lists, not only the solving of problems.

Linked to activity: I-scream lady

Roman times — Page 40

Problem-solving strategies: Logical reasoning / Trial and improvement

Practise dividing the given total by the number of parts it should have. Read the instructions very carefully to be sure that all guides are being followed.

Linked to activity: Mother Bird

Colour me smart — Page 41

Problem-solving strategy: Logical reasoning

This requires thought before action. The children need to carefully consider each move before they make it. Should they require a new start, allow use of suppled squared paper to try again. Some children may enjoy finding several different solutions. Remember: the process and the thinking demonstrated are more important than solutions.

Linked to activity: Star Quest

Crummy calculator — CD only

Problem-solving strategy: Logical reasoning

A thinking exercise of everyday problem solving. Ask the children: *How can you do something when the mechanism does not work?* Tell them there is always a way. These problems reinforce some number concepts such as 9 × 6 = 9 × 5 + 9 × 1. This would be one way to cope with the malfunction of the '6' on the calculator.

Linked to activity: Star Quest

Training for the games — Page 42

Problem-solving strategy: Act it out

Markers such as those from another board game or small counters may be used. Two children can work on this together, each taking the part of a runner.

Linked to activity: Magic girl: tins

The trophy shelf — Page 43

Problem-solving strategy: Act it out

Organised re-arranging should be encouraged. Once the order for the first row is decided, for the second row there should be only one change - eg (a, b, c; a, c, b; - a at the beginning) (b, c, a; b, a, c; - b at the begininng) (c, a, b; c, b, a; - c at the beginning).

Linked to activity: Sven

Lines of history — CD only

Problem-solving strategy: Draw a diagram

Tell the children to turn the page sideways to record the life events. Make each record a shortened note of the narrative (for example, 'Began school'). Discuss what other conclusions the children can draw from the completed timeline.

Money in the bank — CD only

Problem-solving strategy: Work backwards

The unknown is mentioned first, so a symbol is to be chosen for that. Make sure the unknown is clearly understood so that the children know what it is that they are finding, and that this is the first amount in the equation.

Name _____   Date _____

Coin counting

■ To raise money for their special charity, the Kind family in Karingsville have all raided their piggy banks. Can you work out what coins they have donated?

1. Kara has 7 coins totalling £1.50. There are no 5p pieces.
Which coins has she donated?

Estimate 1 _____ = _____

Estimate 2 _____ = _____

Estimate 3 _____ = _____

Answer = _____

2. Kolin has brought in £7.40 with just 4 pairs of coins. What are they?

Estimate 1 _____ = _____

Estimate 2 _____ = _____

Estimate 3 _____ = _____

Answer = _____

3. Kevin brought in a pile of gold coins worth £10. There are three times as many £1 coins as £2 coins. How many of each are there in the pile?

Estimate 1 _____ = _____

Estimate 2 _____ = _____

Estimate 3 _____ = _____

Answer = _____

4. Mr Kind opened his wallet and gave £20 in 3 notes and 3 coins. What could they be?

Estimate 1 _____ = _____

Estimate 2 _____ = _____

Estimate 3 _____ = _____

Answer = _____

Name _____   Date _____

Stickers

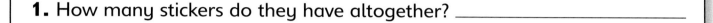

- Holly has 48 stickers.
- Michael has 132 stickers.
- Maria has half as many stickers as Michael.
- Thomas has 214 stickers.

1. How many stickers do they have altogether? _____

2. (a) Thomas gives $\frac{1}{2}$ of his stickers to Holly.

How many stickers does Holly have now? _____

(b) Then Michael gives $\frac{1}{4}$ of his stickers to Thomas.

How many stickers does Thomas have now? _____

How many stickers does Michael have left? _____

(c) Holly then gives $\frac{1}{5}$ of her stickers to Maria.

How many stickers does Maria have now? _____

3. Who has the most stickers at the end of the day? _____

_____

4. What is the difference between the largest amount and the smallest

amount of stickers at the end of the day? _____

Name _____   Date _____

Help the zoo

- Keepum Happy Zoo has six animals to enclose. Each animal must have a tree in its enclosure. The zoo wishes to build only three inside fences.

- Use straws as fences to help the zoo plan where to put the inside fences. There are two different solutions.

= tree

1.

2.

Name _____ Date _____

In the garden

■ Grandma is a keen gardener and each spring she plants neat rows of flowers. Each row contains only one type of flower.

1. How many different arrangements can she make by altering the order of her rows of tulips, daisies and daffodils?

1st row	2nd row	3rd row
_____	_____	_____
_____	_____	_____
_____	_____	_____
_____	_____	_____
_____	_____	_____
_____	_____	_____

Answer _____

2. Grandma has many garden tasks to do. She needs to water, weed, sweep and clip. She can do two things per day, each day for four days. Show two ways that she can plan her jobs so that they all get done twice in the four days.

(a) Mon _____ **(b)** Mon _____

Wed _____ Wed _____

Fri _____ Fri _____

Sat _____ Sat _____

3. Grandma's favourite flowers are roses, lilies and daisies. What possible combinations of these flowers could she have in a bouquet? Use the back of this page to make your list.

Answer _____

Name _____ Date _____

Dogs at work

1. The Council of Woof has to employ more dogs to carry out big projects in the new year. They decide to double the number of workers plus one extra each week. Complete this table to show how many dogs are employed each week in total.

Week 1	Week 2	Week 3	Week 4	Week 5	Week 6	Week 7	Week 8	Week 9	Week 10
1	3	7							

2. The Woof workers are not very careful dogs, and their tools keep getting lost. In week 2, ten tools were lost. But each week, one less tool is lost. Complete the table to show how many tools they have left each week.

Week 1	Week 2	Week 3	Week 4	Week 5	Week 6	Week 7	Week 8	Week 9	Week 10
54									

3. Because of the lost tools, the dogs are paid a little less each week. Study this table and decide how their boss works out how to pay them.

Week 1	Week 2	Week 3	Week 4	Week 5	Week 6	Week 7	Week 8	Week 9	Week 10
£285	£280	£276	£271	£267	£262	£258	£253	£249	£244

_____

_____

4. The dogs are arranged in teams. Use the table in Question 1 to fill in this table. How many dogs are left out when they are in teams of:

	W1	W2	W3	W4	W5	W6	W7	W8	W9	W10
(a) 3										
(b) 4										
(c) 5										
(d) 6										
(e) 7										

Name _____   Date _____

On the farm

- When it's spring on the farm, there is a lot happening. New animals are born and the farmer has many chores to carry out.

1. The five rabbits in the valley each have 1 baby a year. How many rabbits will there be altogether after 3 years?

1st year	**2nd year**	**3rd year**
Rabbits _____	Rabbits _____	Rabbits _____
Babies _____	Babies _____	Babies _____
Total _____	Total _____	Total _____

Answer _____

2. Starting with 160 sheep in August, Farmer Bob has to sell half of them in September, then half of the sheep that are left in October and so on, until he only has 5 left.

In which month will he have 5 left?

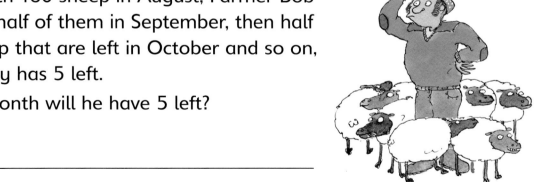

Answer _____

3. The shed roof needs painting, so Farmer Mike begins by doing 8 hours of painting on Tuesday, but can only paint for 7 hours on Wednesday, 6 hours on Thursday and so on, working one hour less every day.

If it takes 33 hours to paint the roof, on what day will he finish?

Answer _____

Name _____   Date _____

Roman times

■ Roman centurions commanded troops of 100 soldiers. Their training was very hard and many soldiers died during their exercises.

1. Each week during training, one more soldier than in the previous week would fail his test.

In week 1, one soldier failed so 99 soldiers were left.

In week 2, two soldiers failed so 97 soldiers were left.

How many weeks had they been training when 72 soldiers were left?

_____

2. On a very long march, the Romans marched in full battle uniform. They found this very tiring and each day would march 2km less than the day before.
On the first day they covered 20km.
After a few days they had covered 68km.

How many days had they been marching? _____

3. Last year, Arturio was the champion in swordsmanship. This year, however, he could not improve. His score decreased by between 1 and 3 points every day of the competition.
After 3 days, his total score was 269.

What were some scores he could have started with? _____

_____

Name _____   Date _____

Colour me smart

1. Colour this board so that every square is a different colour to its neighbouring (adjacent) squares. Use only red, blue and yellow. Same colours may touch at corners only.

How many squares did you colour without putting the same colour on adjacent squares?

_____

2. Place the given symbols in each of the remaining squares so that none is beside, under or above a similar symbol.

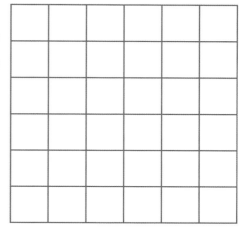

3. Try this bigger one!

What pattern helped you complete the square according to the directions?

_____

_____

_____

_____

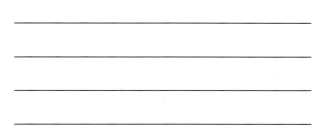

Name _____   Date _____

Training for the games

■ In training for the Mini Marathon in the next Mini Mad Games, Mini Max has to complete 2km jogging, while his older brother Maxi Mak covers 3km.

1. Use counters for each runner to move around the track below.

START

36 km   9 km

27 km   18 km

2. How many kilometres does Mini Max run while his brother runs 36km?

_____

Name _____   Date _____

The trophy shelf

- The Fittnesse family play many sports between them and they are amazingly successful at winning. They have many winner's trophies to keep.

1. Freddy Fittnesse plays football and he won the Best Player Award in 2005, 2006 and 2007. How many different ways can he arrange his trophies on the shelf before they will stand in the same place again? The first row has been done for you. Draw the different arrangements – label the year.

2. Felicity Fittnesse is a champion diver. Her trophies are for the 3m Dive (1), 5m Dive (2), Springboard Dive (3) and Synchronised Dive (4). How many ways can she arrange her trophies? The first row is done for you.

Teacher's name _____

Star Maths Puzzles and Problems diary page

Activity title	Children who used activity	How was activity used	Date used

Activities answers

Dominoes - page 13

1.

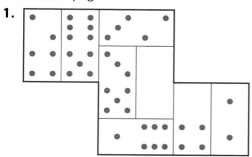

2.

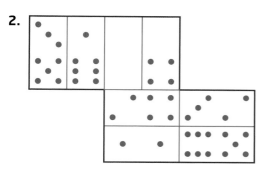

Making tracks - page 15

1. 15km, 5km. Total distance 70km
2. 6km, 2km. Total distance 88km
3. Track 2 is the longest

Magic boy: letters - page 17

1. H
2. J

Elephant enquiry - page 19

1. There are 9 variations.

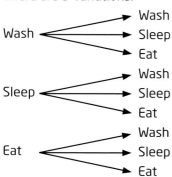

Worm farm - page 21

1. Imram: 7, 14, 21, 28, 35, 42, 49, 56, 63
2. Chloe: 8, 16, 24, 32, 40, 48, 56, 64, 72
3. Ali: 11, 33, 55, 77, 88, 99, 121, 143, 165
4. Zarah: 6, 18, 30, 42, 48, 54, 66, 78, 90

Mr Smoothy - page 23

15 combinations

Litter collectors - page 25 (possible solution)

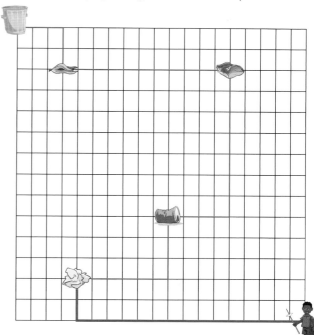

Star Quest - page 27 (possible solution)

1.

multiple of 4	16	24
multiple of 5	10	20

even number	multiple of 2

2.

odd number	19	31
multiple of 3	9	27

less than 20	greater than 20

Simon's tins - page 29

1. Peas
2. Nothing

Problems bank answers

Coin counting – page 34

1. 2 × 50p + 5 × 10p or 1 × 50p + 2 × 10p + 4 × 20p
2. 2 × £2.00, 2 × £1.00, 2 × 50p, 2 × 20p
3. 2 × £2.00, 6 × £1.00
4. 3 × £5 notes, 2 × £2.00, 1 × £1.00

Stickers – page 35

1. 460
2. **(a)** 155
   (b) Thomas has 140; Michael has 99
   (c) 97
3. Holly (Holly: 155, Michael: 99, Maria: 97, Thomas: 140)
4. 58 (155 – 97)

Help at the zoo – page 36
(A mirror image of the first solution below is also correct)

1.
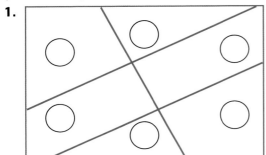

2.
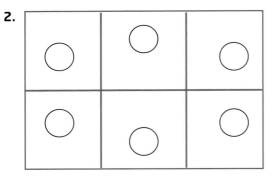

Properties of shapes – CD only

1. **(a)** True   **(b)** True   **(c)** True   **(d)** False
   (e) False   **(f)** False
2. **(a)** False   **(b)** True   **(c)** True   **(d)** False
   (e) False   **(f)** False
3. **(a)** True   **(b)** True   **(c)** True   **(d)** True
   (e) False

In the garden – page 37

1. 6
2. Teacher check
3. 10 (RRR, RRL, RRD, RDD, RLL, RLD, LLL, LLD, LDD, DDD)

Handy trees 1 – CD only

1. cheese + peppers, cheese + mushrooms, cheese + tomatoes; cheese/ham + peppers, cheese/ham + mushrooms, cheese/ham + tomatoes

Handy trees 2 – CD only
(This is one possible solution)

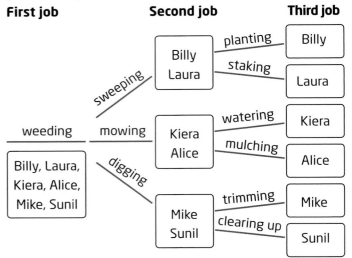

Dogs at work – page 38

1. 15, 31, 63, 127, 255, 511, 1023
2. 44, 35, 27, 20, 14, 9, 5, 2, 0
3. –£5, –£4, –£5, –£4 etc
4. **(a)** 1, 0, 1, 0, 1, 0, 1, 0, 1, 0
   (b) 1, 3, 3, 3, 3, 3, 3, 3, 3, 3
   (c) 1, 3, 2, 0, 1, 3, 2, 0, 1, 3
   (d) 1, 3, 1, 3, 1, 3, 1, 3, 1, 3
   (e) 1, 3, 0, 1, 3, 0, 1, 3, 0, 1

On the farm – page 39

1. 1st year 5, 5, 10; 2nd year 10, 10, 20; 3rd year 20, 20, 40
2. January – 160, 80, 40, 20, 10, 5
3. Sunday – 8, 7, 6, 5, 4, 3 (33 hours)

Problems bank answers

Roman times – page 40
1. 7 weeks
2. 4 days
3. Teacher check

Colour me smart – page 41
Teacher check

Crummy calculator – CD only
There are many answers for each question. Some examples:
1. **(a)** 3 + 3 + 4 + 11
    (b) 6 + 4 + 9 + 8
2. **(a)** 10 ÷ 2 × 27
    (b) 8 × 16 – 8
3. **(a)** 53 – 20 + 1
    (b) 67 + 20 – 1 – 8 + 10 – 1
    (c) 164 – 40 + 1
    (d) 100 – 1 + 17 – 2
4. **(a)** 7 × 2 × 60
    (b) 50 – 5 + 32 – 3 – 1

Training for the games – page 42
Teacher check

The trophy shelf – page 43
1. 6 ways:
    05, 06, 07
    05, 07, 06
    06, 05, 07
    06, 07, 05
    07, 05, 06
    07, 06, 05
2. 24 ways:
    1, 2, 3, 4
    1, 2, 4, 3
    1, 3, 2, 4
    1, 3, 4, 2
    1, 4, 2, 3
    1, 4, 3, 2
    2, 1, 3, 4
    2, 1, 4, 3
    2, 3, 1, 4
    2, 3, 4, 1
    2, 4, 1, 3
    2, 4, 3, 1
    3, 1, 2, 4
    3, 1, 4, 2
    3, 2, 1, 4
    3, 2, 4, 1
    3, 4, 1, 2
    3, 4, 2, 1
    4, 1, 2, 3
    4, 1, 3, 2
    4, 2, 1, 3
    4, 2, 3, 1
    4, 3, 1, 2
    4, 3, 2, 1

Lines of history – CD only
1. **(a)** Teacher check timeline
    (b) False
2. **(a)** Teacher check timeline
    (b) True

Money in the bank – CD only
1. £600
2. £650
3. £1300
2. £10

Also available in this series:

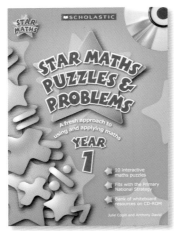

ISBN 978-1407-10031-9

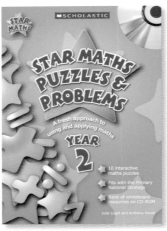

ISBN 978-1407-10032-6

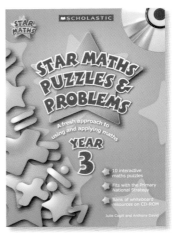

ISBN 978-1407-10033-3

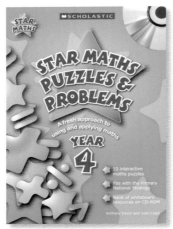

ISBN 978-1407-10034-0

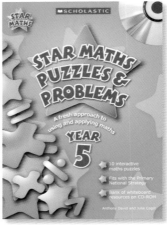

ISBN 978-1407-10035-7

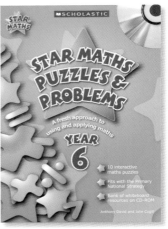

ISBN 978-1407-10036-4

ISBN 978-1407-10007-4

ISBN 978-1407-10008-1

ISBN 978-1407-10009-8

ISBN 978-1407-10010-4

ISBN 978-1407-10011-1

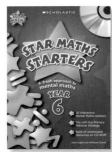

ISBN 978-1407-10012-8

To find out more, call: 0845 603 9091
or visit our website www.scholastic.co.uk